You Can DO IT

health, wellness, and
WEIGHT LOSS

FOR THOSE
WHO HAVE

TRIED everything ELSE

companion journal

MW00608991

NEW YORK TIMES BESTSELLING AUTHOR
JASINDA WILDER

Copyright © 2016 by Jasinda Wilder

All rights reserved.

Cover art and Worksheet Graphics by Sarah Hansen of Okay Creations. Cover art © 2016 by Sarah Hansen.

Formatting by Champagne Formats

Photos by Leah Renee Photography

For full-color recipe photos and printable versions of the worksheets please visit, www.biggirlsdoitrunning.com.

Hi, and welcome to the YOU CAN DO IT companion journal. I'm so glad you are taking steps for a stronger, healthier you! This journal will go along with the book, helping you to keep track of your progress on your journey. Journaling your thoughts as you go will really help you to remember how your body is feeling at every stage, how your body is changing and the fluctuations you may experience. I hope this journal will also inspire you to keep moving, keep focusing on the next meal, and keep enjoying every step of this Wilder Way life. I truly believe that success with this plan is 1% exercise, 9% nutrition, and 90% attitude and determination. Stay positive and take it one day at a time and one meal at a time. Today is the day to change your life!

Health, Fitness, and Kicking Life's Ass!

WEEK 1

WEEK 1 CHALLENGE

This is a slow and steady, from-the-inside-out approach. No quick fixes. We're retraining your body and mind, and that takes time. I don't want you to ever feel frustrated or deprived. I've made these challenges doable for any fitness level, age, or overall health condition.

The first step is to detox your body from the biggest culprits behind the majority of health issues:

First, no sugar at breakfast. None. Focus on protein-rich foods, and completely cut out all sugar before noon. There are sixty-one names for sugar, so please make sure nothing you eat has it hidden in the ingredients. Yes, honey and agave are sugar. You can use stevia as a sweetener—my favorite brands are Pyure and Swerve. You can get them at the grocery store or on Amazon. Try eggs, bacon (remember, fats *ARE* your friend), oatmeal, yogurt (Greek without any added sugar), cottage cheese, toasted Ezekiel brand bread, or cereal with unsweetened almond milk. Berries are great too, so you can load up on those for some natural sweetness. Coffee can be creamed with half and half or heavy whipping cream.

Second, find a 5k to run in the next six months. There are tons of great races out there, so I'm positive you can find one near you. Ask, beg, or coerce a friend or family member to do it with you. If you have kids, I encourage you to include them too—a 5K is fun, healthy, and a great motivator to get moving. Walk if you're not there yet. Or you can try wogging. A 5K is three point one miles from start to finish, so it will take you about an hour, max. You don't even need to start training right now, just commit to running one 5K in your near future. You are *going* to cross a finish line!

WEEK 1 ENCOURAGEMENT

I've studied my ass off trying to figure out why so many of us struggle with excess weight and poor health. I think we fail because we are set up to fail. Why can some people eat whatever they want yet never gain weight, while some of us eat normal amounts and still gain weight? Why won't our bodies work right?

Some of us have had our metabolism literally shut down because of what's being put in our food. We've been eating food we think is healthy, food we're being *told* is healthy, but it's killing us, causing illnesses like diabetes and cancer.

Here's the deal—your current health and weight have nothing to do with your will power or lack there-of. Our bodies are being poisoned to the point of shut-down. Losing weight becomes fairly easy when we cut out chemicals, sugar, fillers, and processed carbohydrates. If you feel an increase in energy by the end of week one, it's a sure sign you were being affected by the sugars in your morning breakfast. Your body is at its most vulnerable in the morning, so it's easy to cause an all-day fog eating the wrong things in the morning. You might not even need as much coffee once this phase is complete and the sugars have been filtered out.

These first six weeks are going to be all about healing; you may not lose ANY weight during this time— none. Why? Because your body is literally turning back on and resetting, and this takes *time*…four to six weeks, in my experience. You may notice a change in your face almost immediately, however, and your pants may get a bit looser. This is because inflammation tends to fade immediately.

YOU CAN DO THIS! Your health is now up to you, but I promise I'll give you all of the tools you'll need to succeed.

This isn't a sprint, it's a marathon.

—JASINDA WILDER

DAY ONE

Slow AND

Steady

On your mark, get
set...GO!

DAY THREE

#WilderWay

DAY FOUR

We'll get
there

DAY FIVE

Keep Moving!

DAY SIX

YOUR BODY WAS
MADE FOR
greatness!

DAY SEVEN

YOU ARE STRONG

I CAN DO THIS!

Positive mind,
strong body,
BEAUTIFUL LIFE

Journal

Think
Positive

How do you feel?

Energy level:

Skin:

Measurements

Arms: Chest: Waist: Hips: Thighs: Lost:

Blood pressure:

Blood sugar:

Cholesterol:

Smile!

(place picture here)

WEEK 2

WEEK 2 CHALLENGE

This week we're getting the sugar out during the day, until dinnertime. This is going to be tough, but you can do it!

Week 2 has two parts: eating and moving. So, with no further ado:

Part One: Eating

Below are my favorite go-to lunches (see my sample diary for more suggestions). Focus on protein, and try to fill up on veggies, nuts, and berries. You can add yogurt too; you have lots of options.

- Salad piled high with meat, cheese, and veggies. We usually do a big chef salad two or three times a week—they're super filling and give you lots of good protein. Remember, lean meats are best but any meat is fine. Heck, throw some bacon in there if you want. It's okay! FAT IS GOOD FOR YOU! Make sure your dressing is low sugar without any crazy additives. Regular old ranch or Italian, things like that. Check your labels!
- Soup. Progresso Lite soups are quick and easy choices for lunch, especially when you throw some WASA crackers in there, or include some Laughing Cow cheese on crackers as a side.
- Mission brand low carb wraps can be used for a rollup sandwich, a quesadilla, or even a pizza—just throw on some tomato sauce, cheese, turkey, pepperoni, and BAM, you've got a healthy pizza! Delicious. Veggies are always great, whether as a side, on a pizza, or however you want to eat them.

Part Two: Movement.

I want you to start moving this week, three times for thirty minutes. I don't even care how you do it. Dance naked in your living room if you want. The only requirement is that you move non-stop for thirty minutes three times this week. Walking is a great option. Don't overwhelm yourself—slow and steady wins the race. This is a change for your whole life, so no need to go crazy. If you love to dance, then I highly suggest Dance Fitness with Jessica. She's got free routines on YouTube that are really fun, so check them out!

WEEK 2 HOMEWORK

You are going to start to documenting your changes this week.

Daily: weigh yourself each morning immediately after your first pee. Write down anything specific you notice about how you are feeling or looking.

Weekly (yes, each week): I want photos. Take some "before photos" from the front and side, and then just your face. These are great for encouragement when the scale isn't moving. Sometimes things are changing shape when your weight stays the same. I also want a waist measurement at the very least. If you want to do more measurements, fine, but I need to have waist measurement. I know this is a lot, but this is a big week and I know you can do it.

Go get 'em!

WEEK 2 ENCOURAGEMENT

This is an 8-week, slow-and-steady plan. I am not expecting any weight loss at this stage and neither should you. In fact, your weight may even go up! That's fine, don't worry! The first four weeks is focused on cleaning up what you eat, and the next four are all about adjusting those foods to get your body into the weight loss mode. I want your weight loss to be for your whole life, not just for a few weeks or months. I want you living and eating in an entirely new way. You didn't become unhealthy over night, and you won't become healthy overnight, so please, please, *PLEASE* give this time. You need your body and mind working together. It's scientific fact that the more quickly you lose weight the less likely you are to keep it off, so let's do this right! Don't freak out and sabotage yourself and the plan.

We'll get there!

One week at a time

DAY ONE

Slow AND

Steady

On your mark, get
set...GO!

DAY TWO

DAY THREE

DAY FOUR

We'll get there

DAY FIVE

Keep Moving!

DAY SIX

YOUR BODY WAS
MADE FOR
greatness!

DAY SEVEN

YOU ARE STRONG

Journal

Think
Positive

Positive mind,
strong body,
BEAUTIFUL LIFE

I CAN DO THIS!

How do you feel?

Energy level:

Skin:

Measurements

Arms: Chest: Waist: Hips: Thighs: Lost:

Blood pressure:

Blood sugar:

Cholesterol:

Smile!
(place picture here)

WEEK 3

WEEK 3 CHALLENGE

This is a big week. I know this challenge is going to be tough, so it's the *only* thing I'm asking you to do this week.

Cut out *all* **non-stevia-sweetened soda and sugary drinks.** You don't need them and they're doing incalculable harm to your body. The good news is; I have a few fun beverages for you to try this week.

I know you can do this!

Just say no to junk!

Stick with no sugar until dinnertime—after dinner it is all yours…this week.

Stick with thirty minutes of movement three times a week.

Keep tracking your weight every day.

You've got this! Lots more to come. We've only just begun.

WEEK 3 ENCOURAGEMENT

Do you drink Green Tea? If not, you should! But drinking any tea will be great for you. Add some cinnamon and ginger to help with the detox and to keep your blood sugars level. I usually have some green tea about three in the afternoon, with a few nuts to keep me satisfied until dinner.

My afternoon tea treat, Wilder Tea:

- Steep your favorite green or black tea (make sure it doesn't have added gluten)
- Add some unsweetened vanilla almond milk
- Sprinkle on some cinnamon (this is going to help you fight sugar cravings)
- Add some ginger (so good for you! I buy it in both liquid and powder forms)
- Add a little Stevia if you are craving some sweetness.

Pro Tip: Don't forget to drink lots of water. Drinking water when you wake up in the morning will jump start your metabolism; add some lemon to get that fire burning!

DAY ONE

Slow and

Steady

DAY TWO

On your mark, get set...GO!

DAY THREE

DAY FOUR

We'll get there

DAY FIVE

Keep Moving!

DAY SIX

YOUR BODY WAS
MADE FOR
greatness!

DAY SEVEN

YOU ARE STRONG

Journal

Think
Positive

I CAN DO THIS!

Positive mind,
strong body,
BEAUTIFUL LIFE

How do you feel?

Energy level:

Skin:

Measurements

Arms: Chest: Waist: Hips: Thighs: Lost:

Blood pressure:

Blood sugar:

Cholesterol:

Smile!
(place picture here)

WEEK 4

WEEK 4 CHALLENGE

This is a big one, so hold on to your Spanx!

This week we are cutting out ALL sugar and refined carbs. Kiss them all goodbye, because you don't need them—they're killing you! That's a bold statement, but it's the absolute truth. They're hurting you and you no longer want that, you want to be healthy and strong. This week you should see a pretty big difference in your face, so make sure to take a photo or two. All your inflammation is going to go away pretty quickly once we get all the junk out of your system. Get excited! Big things are about to happen.

The second part of the challenge this week is about movement. I'm not changing the three times a week movement rule, but I do want one of those days spent either walking, wogging, or jogging. Thirty minutes of your feet hitting the pavement. I don't care how fast or slow you go, just get out and do it. Even short bursts of wogging and getting your heart rate up is great for you. Try it!

You've got this!

WEEK 4 HOMEWORK REMINDER

Daily: I want you to weigh yourself each morning right after your first pee. I also want you to note anything specific about how you are feeling or looking.

Weekly: I want photos. Take some "before photos"; front and side views, and then also just your face. These are great for comparison and encouragement when the scale isn't moving. Sometimes things are changing shape when your weight stays the same. Remember to take your waist measurement. If you want to take more measurements, go right ahead, but make sure you do that waist measurement.

WEEK 4 ENCOURAGEMENT

Don't cry into your Wilder oats just yet! There are so many good things you can have this week! Low carb mission wraps, brown rice, sweet potatoes, sprouted breads, Dreamfields brand pasta, oats, quinoa, nut flours, and carbs that naturally occur in fruits, nuts, veggies and beans. You'll get the hang of this. It's okay for progress to take some time. It *will* happen and you *will* get there. Just stick with me and don't give up.

You are doing fantastic!

DAY ONE

Slow and
Steady

On your mark, get set...GO!

DAY THREE

DAY FOUR

We'll get
there

DAY FIVE

Keep Moving!

DAY SIX

YOUR BODY WAS
MADE FOR
greatness!

DAY SEVEN

YOU ARE STRONG

I CAN DO THIS!

Journal

Think
Positive

Positive mind,
strong body,
BEAUTIFUL LIFE

How do you feel?

Energy level:

Skin:

Measurements

Arms: Chest: Waist: Hips: Thighs: Lost:

Blood pressure:

Blood sugar:

Cholesterol:

Smile!
(place picture here)

WEEK 5

WEEK 5 CHALLENGE

BLACK PLATE WEEK

Remember, black plates are for proteins and fats; white plates are for proteins and carbs.

As I already said, our bodies have difficulty keeping our metabolism running steadily when we consume both high fats and high carbs in the same meal. So, this week and next week we are in fats and carbs boot camp. This week is the harder of the two, since it's BLACK PLATE WEEK. This means you won't be eating ANY carbs for the next week—your *only* bread choice is Mission brand low carb wraps.

No other grains.

AT ALL.

I'm watching you.

The only fruits allowed are berries, lemons and limes. Don't cry, though, because you can load up on cheese, sour cream, meats, nuts, and Lily's chocolate. Please be sure to take a look at my **BLACK PLATE WEEK SHEET** for full food options.

KEEP MOVING

You also need to walk, run or wog for as long as you can this week. If possible, I want you to try my Wilder Wog, described in the FAQ section. Journal about it at home, and then let me know how it went. I want specifics like, "I walked for twenty minutes and I wogged for ten. It was really hard and I almost died and I hate you."

You can do this.

Be prepared to kick some serious ass.

Keep up on your daily weigh-ins and measurements! Change is a-comin'.

It's going to be worth it, I promise!

WEEK 5 ENCOURAGEMENT

My dream is to start a revolution, one in which we all stop dieting and begin a new regimen of eating that we will stick to for our whole lives. One where we start feeling good about our bodies, where we have positive self-images and we walk with our heads held high, proud of what we've accomplished. In this health and wellness revolution, everyone believes they can run—and they even get excited about it. I long for the day when we aren't suffering from horrible diseases like diabetes, PCOS and ADHD. I want the whole world to know that if *I* can do it, they can do it, too.

Change is a -comin'

DAY ONE

Slow AND

Steady

On your mark, get set...GO!

DAY THREE

DAY FOUR

We'll get there

DAY FIVE

Keep Moving!

DAY SIX

YOUR BODY WAS
MADE FOR
greatness!

DAY SEVEN

YOU ARE STRONG

I CAN DO THIS!

Journal

Think
Positive

Positive mind,
strong body,
BEAUTIFUL LIFE

How do you feel?

Energy level:

Skin:

Measurements

Arms: Chest: Waist: Hips: Thighs: Lost:

Blood pressure:

Blood sugar:

Cholesterol:

Smile!

(place picture here)

The three possible plates for your meal

THE BLACK PLATE

Protein + Fat(s)

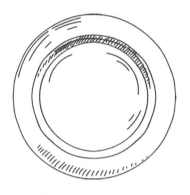

THE WHITE PLATE

Protein + Carbohydrates and starches

THE GRAY PLATE

Protein + Fat(s) + Carbohydrates/starches
(4-5 of these per week max)

WEEK 6

WEEK 6 CHALLENGE

WHITE PLATE WEEK

Remember, black plates are for proteins and fats; white plates are for proteins and carbs.

This week is the same concept as last week, except we're changing plate colors; get out your white plates, girls, because this week the carbs are in the house!

Carbs have a bit of a bad reputation, but they aren't the bad nutrient everyone makes them out to be. You just need to find the *right* carbs to put on your plate—that's what we're doing this week, focusing on *healthy* carbs. Which means all other kinds of carbs are dead to you…FOREVER!

The stars of the show this week are sprouted breads and cereals, old-fashioned oats, fruit, brown rice, beans, and potatoes. These are the good carbs; please be sure to check my graphic on white plates for the full list.

This week you need to stick to *lean* meats and proteins. What does that mean? Chicken and turkey breast, fish, venison, lean ground turkey and chicken (96% protein or higher), lean deli meats and ground beef—85% lean or better (drained). Make sure you stick to low fats in your food this week because we don't want to have any of our black plate friends accidentally turn your white plates gray— that is *not* allowed.

This week might seem hard, but I know you can do it. Just focus on lean protein and don't forget your veggies, as you'll need lots of fiber after the full week of fats last week.

Yes, you can still have Progresso light soup.

It will be okay, I promise!

You've got this!

WEEK 6 HOMEWORK:

Keep taking photos and measurements, and don't forget to journal. This is your health journey, so we want good records to show how far you've come!

This week we're also going to amp up your training. I need you to step it up...literally. Continue with the three movement sessions of at least thirty minutes each this week. Two of those *have* to be walking/wogging/jogging for as long as you can, as far as you can. I don't care what those numbers are, but you HAVE to try. You're going to be running a 5k soon, so we need to get you ready. Now get going! Get on your workout gear, ladies, because it's time to get moving!

WEEK 6 ENCOURAGEMENT

Are you starting to feel the changes in your body? Maybe your weight has gone down a bit, or maybe it's gone up. Regardless of the number, you're seeing and feeling *something*. This week and next week we're setting the metabolic pendulum into full swing. Think of your body as a beautiful beach: the black plate and white plate weeks will put the waves into motion. It's okay if you see your weight start to creep up a bit, that's normal. Just look for an overall, long-term downward trend. As we get into the next few weeks you'll see that now that your metabolism has been jump-started, keeping it revving will become easier and easier. Just keep on keeping on, have faith in your body and in the plan, and don't stop moving!

YOU'VE GOT THIS!

DAY ONE

Slow AND

Steady

DAY TWO

On your mark, get set...GO!

DAY THREE

DAY FOUR

We'll get

there

DAY FIVE

Keep Moving!

DAY SIX

YOUR BODY WAS
MADE FOR
greatness!

DAY SEVEN

YOU ARE STRONG

Positive mind,
strong body,
BEAUTIFUL LIFE

I CAN DO THIS!

Journal

Think Positive

How do you feel?

Energy level:

Skin:

Measurements

Arms: Chest: Waist: Hips: Thighs: Lost:

Blood pressure:

Blood sugar:

Cholesterol:

Smile!
(place picture here)

WEEK 7

WEEK 7 CHALLENGE

MIXING UP YOUR PLATES!

Remember, black plates are for proteins and fats; white plates are for proteins and carbs.

This is the week you've been waiting for! Now we start to mix up your plates. Throughout the last two weeks you've probably been able to see how your body responds differently to the protein plus fats combination, and the protein plus carbs combination. Now we're going to keep mixing it up so your body never knows what's coming.

An important note before we get started, though, is that you can't do this halfway. This *isn't* Atkins. Think about these two different plates like a swinging pendulum. As far as you swing in one direction, you need to swing just as far in the opposite direction. Don't be scared of good carbohydrates! Your body needs them. Swinging back and forth will keep the waves of your metabolism moving.

Try these daily plans this week and find out which one works best for you. Next week you'll be totally freestyling your plates, and even mixing them up a bit.

So, for Week 7, your job is to adhere to the following in terms of your food intake:

Day 1: Black only all day
Day 2: White only all day
Day 3: Black, Black, White—breakfast, lunch, dinner
Day 4: White, White, Black—breakfast, lunch, dinner
Day 5: Black, White, Black—breakfast, lunch, dinner
Day 6: White, Black, White—breakfast, lunch, dinner
Day 7: White, Black, Black—breakfast, lunch, dinner

As well, I want you wogging three times this week, for as long as you can. Stop and walk if you have to, but I want you to really push your limits this week.

Don't forget, your body was made for greatness!

WEEK 7 ENCOURAGEMENT:

Can you see the finish line? You're *so* close to reaching your goal! Your metabolism is running full force this week, you're wogging and starting to get strong. This is the time to journal. Remember how you're feeling, and don't forget it's only been less than two months. Can you believe how far you have come? Remember where you started, and keep an eye on where you're going! That 5k will be here before you know it!

GET OUT AND WOG!

DAY ONE

Slow AND

Steady

DAY TWO

DAY THREE

#WilderWay

DAY FOUR

We'll get
there

DAY FIVE

Keep Moving!

DAY SIX

YOUR BODY WAS
MADE FOR
greatness!

DAY SEVEN

YOU ARE STRONG

I CAN DO THIS!

Positive mind,
strong body,
BEAUTIFUL LIFE

Journal

Think
Positive

How do you feel?

Energy level:

Skin:

Measurements

Arms: Chest: Waist: Hips: Thighs: Lost:

Blood pressure:

Blood sugar:

Cholesterol:

Smile!
(place picture here)

WEEK 8

WEEK 8 CHALLENGE

PLATES YOUR WAY!

Remember, black plates are for proteins and fats; white plates are for proteins and carbs.

Eating:
Congratulations! You made it to Week 8! Four weeks of detox, three weeks of learning plate styles and combinations, and now this final week where we get your metabolism revving high and on fire—not just for a few weeks or months, but for the rest of your life!

This week is all about learning how to keep it going on your own.

All you need to do is pick your plate for each meal; ask yourself which plate do you want for this meal? Which color will you do for breakfast tomorrow, or dinner on Thursday? This is the easy part, really, because you are totally in control. You can mix it up however you want!

A word of caution, though: don't devise your meal plan to include fifty plates of gray! Gray plates are, of course, plates that combine carbs, fats, and proteins. You don't want too many gray plates in your weekly plan—I try to limit mine to about three or four per week, max. Gray plates are totally fine in moderation, and they will help keep you on the right path, just don't get too dependent on them. We need to keep that pendulum always moving, those waves always crashing.

Now that we have your body working *for* you rather than against you, you have to keep working for your body. How many black plates and how many white plates should you do per week? Well, that depends on you; your body will tell you what it needs. I try to get in one white plate each day, usually for breakfast, as I've found this the best way to keep my metabolism humming at a nice pace. You may find yourself needing more white plates or fewer, depending on how your body responds.

I do think, however, that the more you increase physical activity the more white plates you'll probably need, since they're a great energy source. If you're doing a long or strenuous run, I would make sure you have a white plate dinner the night before and then again for breakfast that morning—you'll need those carbs! I do average more black plates than white, and more white than gray, but that's just what works best for me as a borderline diabetic. Everyone is different; so let your body dictate what's best for you.

If you stall in terms of weight loss, my best advice is to mix things up. Keep changing up the plate colors and that'll get things moving. Don't worry when you have those stalls, though—your body just needs time to adjust. I hit a plateau about every fifteen to twenty pounds I lose.

Don't forget to hydrate.

Eat your veggies.

EAT! Not eating enough, regardless of plate color, will only slow your progress. Try to get to a place where you're neither under-eating nor over-eating, and don't forget that protein is *always* the focus.

These basic principles will keep your body moving and healthy.

Movement:

Your movement this week is easy: Three days of wogging, working up to a 5k!

- Day 1: one easy mile. Walk first and then try to move into a wog and keep wogging as much as you can.
- Day 2: two miles. Start with a nice brisk walk and work into your wog. Wog to the end. Don't forget to "beast mode" those last few minutes!
- Day 3: three miles! Yes, *three*. You can totally just walk the first one, nice and easy. Mile two, get into a comfortable wogging pace. Bring it back down to a walk whenever you need. Mile three is for beast mode: push yourself hard! Find out how much wogging you can do all the way to the finish line. You've totally got this 5k in the bag!

I knew you could do it, even when you didn't!

Now, just keep it up on your own.

Keep training and keep moving your body.

You're kicking ass!

WEEK 8 HOMEWORK:

Keep documenting your changes.

Daily: Keep weighing yourself each morning right after your first pee. I also want you to note anything specific you noticed about how you're feeling or looking.

Weekly: I want photos. Take some "before photos"; front and side, and then also just your face. Use these photos for comparison purposes when the scale isn't moving. Sometimes things are changing shape when your weight stays the same. Keep up with those waist measurements and if you want to do more measurements, fine, but don't stop putting that measuring tape around your waist. I would love to hear your story and see your photos! Please consider emailing them to me, or sharing on social media. www.

WEEK 8 ENCOURAGEMENT:

Give your body as long as it takes to reach a place of strength and health. How long will that be? Eight more weeks? Eight more months? Eighteen months? It doesn't matter! The only goal is good health. If there's anything I've learned on this journey, it's to give my body time and grace: this isn't a sprint, it's a marathon. Don't worry if you trip up a few times along the way—just pick yourself up and keep on wogging. You've made all the right steps toward good health, now keep focused on the next meal, the next day, and the next run.

I'm so proud of you!

Pro tip: I tend to "Suzan Sommersize" my fruit, meaning eating it in moderation and eating it alone, unless it's berries, lemons, or limes. I've found loading fruit in with other carbs is just too much sugar for me, and I suspect you may find the same thing to be true for you.

Keep Going!

DAY ONE

Slow AND Steady

On your mark, get
set...GO!

DAY THREE

DAY FOUR

We'll get

there

DAY FIVE

Keep Moving!

DAY SIX

YOUR BODY WAS
MADE FOR
greatness!

DAY SEVEN

YOU ARE STRONG

Journal

Think Positive

I CAN DO THIS!

Positive mind,
strong body,
BEAUTIFUL LIFE

How do you feel?

Energy level:

Skin:

Measurements

Arms: Chest: Waist: Hips: Thighs: Lost:

Blood pressure:

Blood sugar:

Cholesterol:

SMOOTHIES

JASINDA'S RISE AND SHINE SHAKE

1 scoop Jay Robb Tropical Dreamsicle protein powder

1 scoop collagen

½ tsp vitamin C powder

½ tsp stevia

2 cups unsweetened vanilla almond milk

1 handful of frozen strawberries

½ container Triple Zero yogurt (I like banana)

splash of vanilla extract

optional: a handful of spinach or other greens

JACK'S CHOCOLATE PEANUT BUTTER DREAM SHAKE

Scoop of Jay Robb chocolate protein powder

A cup or two of unsweetened Almond milk (you can also use plain unsweetened almond milk and add vanilla extract)

Lily's chips, Lily's bar chocolate, or other dark chocolate or cocoa—add as much as you want; I throw in about a handful of chips

One handful of frozen spinach

One handful of ice

One or two spoonfuls of natural peanut butter

*(can also add additional stevia or swerve to taste)

Nothing will stop me. I can do this!

WILD, HOT, AND SPICY SOUP
(THIS MAKES ONE LARGE POT! GREAT TO HEAT UP LATER IN THE WEEK TOO!)

One box container of bone broth (so good for you!)

6 oz of water

2lbs of any meat of your choice; we love shredded chicken for this one.

Add all of your favorite spices! Some of our favorites to add are Cumin, onion powder, chili powder, cayenne, garlic powder, or chipotle. If you want to get really crazy, add them all! Don't forget a bit of mineral salt too.

We always add lots of our favorite Simple Girl hot sauce. This stuff is amazing and we usually are pretty generous in adding it because my family likes it hot. Add to your own tastes.

I also love to add veggies for fiber; I usually use chopped tomato and some celery.

Since my husband hates most other veggies, I put them in a blender with a jar of our favorite Field Day salsa, a few tablespoons of coconut oil, and a half scoop of collagen. Whatever your kids and husband don't know about the soup won't hurt them!

I sometimes add a bit of 1/3rd fat cream cheese as well. You can top with a garnish of cheese, blue corn chips, and/or 0%-fat Greek yogurt. This goes great with a few Wasa and keeps you full all day long.

FANCY STRAWBERRY CUPCAKES

This could also be made into a cake; this was a special request for Nanny Karri's birthday.
It was a big hit! You can top with fresh strawberries and make this a super yummy fancy treat.

Pre-heat oven to 350 degrees

Combine and whisk dry ingredients:

Cake: 1/2 cup Almond Flour and ½ cup coconut flour

1 cup oat fiber

One scoop Jay Robb strawberry protein powder

2 ½ tsp. baking powder

3 T Pyure

2 T Swerve (sweeten to taste)

½ xanthan gum

½ tsp salt

Combine and beat with wet ingredients:

One big spoonful of strawberry all fruit jelly

One big spoonful of ⅓ fat cream cheese

½ cup salted butter, soft

4 eggs

1 cup water

¾ cup egg whites

½ tsp vanilla extract

1 tsp strawberry extract

a few drops of natural red food coloring to make the batter a pretty pink

Spread into muffin tin with liners and bake for 18-20 minutes.

I let these refrigerate over night and then frost them.

If these aren't sweet enough for you, you can always sprinkle more of the Swerve on top of the cake before frosting.

Makes 18 cupcakes.

Frosting:

2 cups heavy whipping cream

1 generous Tbsp. swerve confectioner's sugar (sweeten to taste)

dash of salt

dash of vanilla extract

dash of strawberry extract

2 spoonfuls of strawberry all fruit jelly

2 -3 drops of food coloring to make it pink

Whip, and whip it GOOD! This does take some time but you want it to be a nice creamy texture. I chill this frosting and then spread generously over my cupcakes. You can add a bit of ⅓ fat cream cheese if you want it a bit more dense.

CONVERSIONS

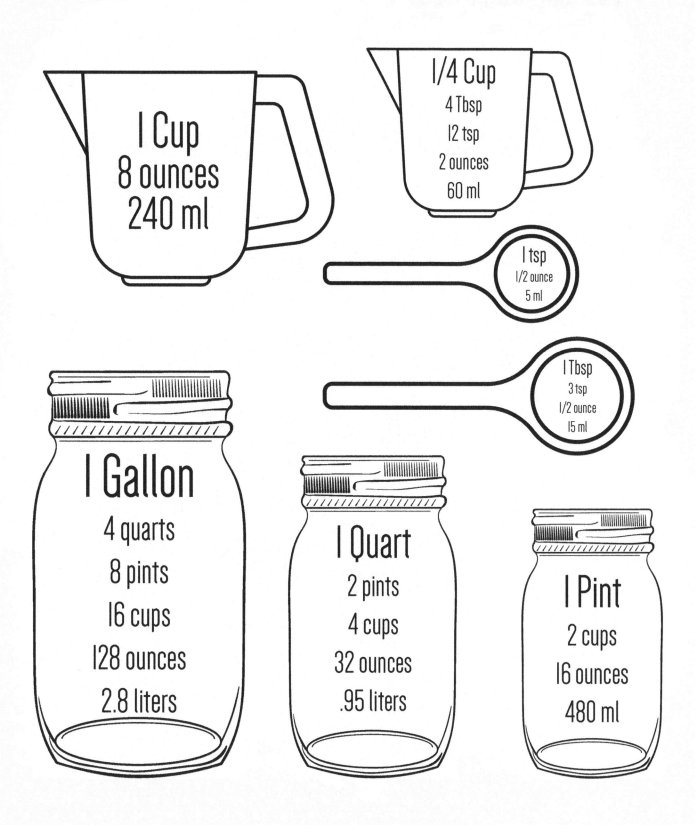

1 Cup
8 ounces
240 ml

1/4 Cup
4 Tbsp
12 tsp
2 ounces
60 ml

1 tsp
1/2 ounce
5 ml

1 Tbsp
3 tsp
1/2 ounce
15 ml

1 Gallon
4 quarts
8 pints
16 cups
128 ounces
2.8 liters

1 Quart
2 pints
4 cups
32 ounces
.95 liters

1 Pint
2 cups
16 ounces
480 ml

Regular Sugar Stevia (blends)

5tsp ⟶ 2tsp

¼ cup ⟶ I TBSP + I tsp

1/3 cup ⟶ 2 TBSP

½ cup ⟶ 3 TBSP + I tsp

I cup ⟶ 6 TBSP

Favorite Recipes

Favorite Recipes

Favorite Recipes

How I'm feeling

date:

Hello beautiful!

"God meant for my body to be healthy and strong.
I am worth the time it will take to make myself stronger and healthier.

It won't be easy, *but it will be worth it.*
Yes, it's okay to do this for those who love me as well, but this is for me.
I was beautiful then, I am beautiful now, and I will be beautiful tomorrow.

I CAN DO THIS.

I can do this despite feeling like I can't, or that I've been told I can't.
My body is beautiful at any size.
My body is going to be unstoppable when I'm healthier and stronger, so watch out!
NOTHING WILL DEFINE ME.

Nothing will stop me.
I CAN DO THIS!"

How to Measure

First, love yourself. You might not be happy with these numbers, and you might even be scared to know them, but they are a place to start.

Pull the tape to circle your waist (sort of like a belt would) at your natural waistline, which is located above your belly button and below your rib cage. (If you bend to the side, the crease that forms is your natural waistline.)

Thigh: Measure the circumference of the fullest part of your thigh. Wrap the tape measure around your thigh from front to back and then around to the front.

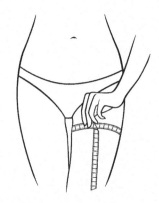

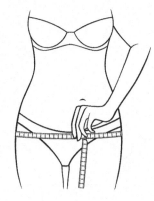

Hips: Start at one hip and wrap the tape measure around your booty, around the other hip, and back to where you started. Make sure the tape is over the largest part of your butt. Make sure the tape is level back there!

8 WEEK CHALLENGE

Measurements

	arms	chest	waist	hips	thighs	lost
1						
2						
3						
4						
5						
6						
7						
8						

you can do it!

Measurements

	arms	chest	waist	hips	thighs	* lost
JAN						
FEB						
MAR						
APR						
MAY						
JUNE						
JULY						
AUG						
SEPT						
OCT						
NOV						
DEC						
total lost						

You are doing fantastic!

Measurements

	arms	chest	waist	hips	thighs	" lost
JAN						
FEB						
MAR						
APR						
MAY						
JUNE						
JULY						
AUG						
SEPT						
OCT						
NOV						
DEC						
total lost						

You are doing fantastic!

Running Log

date	time	distance	walking speed	running speed	notes

get out and wog!

Running Log

date	time	distance	walking speed	running speed	notes

get out and wog!

Running Log

date	time	distance	walking speed	running speed	notes

get out and wog!

Running Log

date	time	distance	walking speed	running speed		notes

get out and wog!

First 5k!

date:

Race name:

Time:

Bib number:

Who was there with me:

How I felt:

Other 5K's

Race Name	Date	✓

CROSS THE FINISH LINE!

Weekly Meal Planner

	breakfast	lunch	snack	dinner
SUNDAY	☐ white plate ☐ black plate	☐ white plate ☐ black plate	☐ white plate ☐ black plate	☐ white plate ☐ black plate
MONDAY	☐ white plate ☐ black plate	☐ white plate ☐ black plate	☐ white plate ☐ black plate	☐ white plate ☐ black plate
TUESDAY	☐ white plate ☐ black plate	☐ white plate ☐ black plate	☐ white plate ☐ black plate	☐ white plate ☐ black plate
WEDNESDAY	☐ white plate ☐ black plate	☐ white plate ☐ black plate	☐ white plate ☐ black plate	☐ white plate ☐ black plate
THURSDAY	☐ white plate ☐ black plate	☐ white plate ☐ black plate	☐ white plate ☐ black plate	☐ white plate ☐ black plate
FRIDAY	☐ white plate ☐ black plate	☐ white plate ☐ black plate	☐ white plate ☐ black plate	☐ white plate ☐ black plate
SATURDAY	☐ white plate ☐ black plate	☐ white plate ☐ black plate	☐ white plate ☐ black plate	☐ white plate ☐ black plate

Weekly Meal Planner

	breakfast	lunch	snack	dinner
SUNDAY	☐ white plate ☐ black plate	☐ white plate ☐ black plate	☐ white plate ☐ black plate	☐ white plate ☐ black plate
MONDAY	☐ white plate ☐ black plate	☐ white plate ☐ black plate	☐ white plate ☐ black plate	☐ white plate ☐ black plate
TUESDAY	☐ white plate ☐ black plate	☐ white plate ☐ black plate	☐ white plate ☐ black plate	☐ white plate ☐ black plate
WEDNESDAY	☐ white plate ☐ black plate	☐ white plate ☐ black plate	☐ white plate ☐ black plate	☐ white plate ☐ black plate
THURSDAY	☐ white plate ☐ black plate	☐ white plate ☐ black plate	☐ white plate ☐ black plate	☐ white plate ☐ black plate
FRIDAY	☐ white plate ☐ black plate	☐ white plate ☐ black plate	☐ white plate ☐ black plate	☐ white plate ☐ black plate
SATURDAY	☐ white plate ☐ black plate	☐ white plate ☐ black plate	☐ white plate ☐ black plate	☐ white plate ☐ black plate

Weekly Meal Planner

	breakfast	lunch	snack	dinner
SUNDAY	white plate · black plate	white plate · black plate	white plate · black plate	white plate · black plate
MONDAY	white plate · black plate	white plate · black plate	white plate · black plate	white plate · black plate
TUESDAY	white plate · black plate	white plate · black plate	white plate · black plate	white plate · black plate
WEDNESDAY	white plate · black plate	white plate · black plate	white plate · black plate	white plate · black plate
THURSDAY	white plate · black plate	white plate · black plate	white plate · black plate	white plate · black plate
FRIDAY	white plate · black plate	white plate · black plate	white plate · black plate	white plate · black plate
SATURDAY	white plate · black plate	white plate · black plate	white plate · black plate	white plate · black plate

Weekly Meal Planner

	breakfast	lunch	snack	dinner
SUNDAY	☐ white plate ☐ black plate	☐ white plate ☐ black plate	☐ white plate ☐ black plate	☐ white plate ☐ black plate
MONDAY	☐ white plate ☐ black plate	☐ white plate ☐ black plate	☐ white plate ☐ black plate	☐ white plate ☐ black plate
TUESDAY	☐ white plate ☐ black plate	☐ white plate ☐ black plate	☐ white plate ☐ black plate	☐ white plate ☐ black plate
WEDNESDAY	☐ white plate ☐ black plate	☐ white plate ☐ black plate	☐ white plate ☐ black plate	☐ white plate ☐ black plate
THURSDAY	☐ white plate ☐ black plate	☐ white plate ☐ black plate	☐ white plate ☐ black plate	☐ white plate ☐ black plate
FRIDAY	☐ white plate ☐ black plate	☐ white plate ☐ black plate	☐ white plate ☐ black plate	☐ white plate ☐ black plate
SATURDAY	☐ white plate ☐ black plate	☐ white plate ☐ black plate	☐ white plate ☐ black plate	☐ white plate ☐ black plate

Weekly Meal Planner

	breakfast	lunch	snack	dinner
SUNDAY	□ white plate □ black plate	□ white plate □ black plate	□ white plate □ black plate	□ white plate □ black plate
MONDAY	□ white plate □ black plate	□ white plate □ black plate	□ white plate □ black plate	□ white plate □ black plate
TUESDAY	□ white plate □ black plate	□ white plate □ black plate	□ white plate □ black plate	□ white plate □ black plate
WEDNESDAY	□ white plate □ black plate	□ white plate □ black plate	□ white plate □ black plate	□ white plate □ black plate
THURSDAY	□ white plate □ black plate	□ white plate □ black plate	□ white plate □ black plate	□ white plate □ black plate
FRIDAY	□ white plate □ black plate	□ white plate □ black plate	□ white plate □ black plate	□ white plate □ black plate
SATURDAY	□ white plate □ black plate	□ white plate □ black plate	□ white plate □ black plate	□ white plate □ black plate

Weekly Meal Planner

	breakfast	lunch	snack	dinner
SUNDAY	white plate ☐ black plate	white plate ☐ black plate	white plate ☐ black plate	white plate ☐ black plate
MONDAY	white plate ☐ black plate	white plate ☐ black plate	white plate ☐ black plate	white plate ☐ black plate
TUESDAY	white plate ☐ black plate	white plate ☐ black plate	white plate ☐ black plate	white plate ☐ black plate
WEDNESDAY	white plate ☐ black plate	white plate ☐ black plate	white plate ☐ black plate	white plate ☐ black plate
THURSDAY	white plate ☐ black plate	white plate ☐ black plate	white plate ☐ black plate	white plate ☐ black plate
FRIDAY	white plate ☐ black plate	white plate ☐ black plate	white plate ☐ black plate	white plate ☐ black plate
SATURDAY	white plate ☐ black plate	white plate ☐ black plate	white plate ☐ black plate	white plate ☐ black plate

Sugar
AKA

Agave nectar
Dehydrated cane juice
Date sugar
Golden sugar
GOLDEN SYRUP
Barley malt
Brown sugar
Icing sugar
Maltol Fructose
Sweet Sorghum
Cane sugar
Buttered syrup
Panocha Molasses
Fruit juice concentrate
Sucrose
Sugar (granulated)
Coconut palm sugar
BARBADOS SUGAR
Corn syrup solids
Turbinado sugar
Evaporated cane juice
Cane juice
Invert sugar
Powdered sugar
Free-flowing brown sugars
Dextrose
Maltose
Palm sugar
Corn syrup
Fruit juice
HFCS (High-Fructose Corn Syrup)
Yellow sugar
CORN SWEETENER
CAROB SYRUP
Demerara sugar
Malt syrup
Glucose solids
Grape sugar
Malt syrup
Coconut sugar
Rice syrup
Sorghum Syrup
TREACLE Confectioner's sugar
Dextrin
Saccharose
GLUCOSE SYRUP
Mannose
Maltodextrin
Barley malt syrup
Cane juice crystals
Raw sugar
Castor sugar
Refiner's syrup
Muscovado
Honey
Caramel
BEET SUGAR
Maple syrup

Grocery List

Oikos Triple 0 yogurt

Ezekiel bread

Silver Hills bread

Unique Sprouted Splits whole grain wheat pretzels

Wasa crackers (Sourdough and Rye)

Chunkie Dunkies cookies (the Stevia sweetened varieties)

Applegate meat

Lily's chocolate

Dr. John's candies***

Pur Gum***

Jay Robb whey isolate protein powder

Horizon Organics

Laughing Cow cheese

Crofter's Just Fruit spread

Bragg's Liquid Aminos, ACV, and dressing

Dreamfield's pasta

Califia Farms milk and creamer

Fairlife milk

Bryer's Carb Smart ice cream and bars*

Garden of Eatin' baked blue corn chips

Hope Foods Guacamole

Mary's Gone Crackers

Mission whole wheat low carb wraps

Joseph's low carb Lavash bread

Kerry's Gold butter without canola oil

Real Good pizza

Kodiak power cakes – a great choice for the kids

Quest protein bars*

Kirkland Brand (Costco) generic Quest protein bars

Bai drinks and soda

Progresso light soup (non-cream based variety)

Ezekiel cereal

Wholesome or Plantation Blackstrap molassses

Lakanto maple flavored syrup

Primal Kitchen avocado mayo**

Simple Girl sauces

Uncle Sam's cereal

PB & Me**

FLAVORGOD seasonings

Sir Kensington mustard and ketchup

Organic Hope Guacamole

Zevia soda

Blue Sky ZERO soda

Vitamin Water Zero

Nut Pods creamer**

Naturals Deli meat

Sweet leaf flavored sweetener and water enhancer

Naturally Nutty almond and peanut butter

True Lemon and True lime water powers and flavors

La Croix

Natural Mate Sweetener **

Pyure Sweetener

Swerve Sweetener

Bolthouse dressing

Halo Top ice cream

*may contain sucralose

** we have only found these on Amazon

*** may contain xylitol, a sweetener that can be fatal to pets

Grocery List

- [ ] Nut pods creamer—mix with stevia for a great alternative to creamer
- [ ] Natural deli meats without nitrates
- [ ] Fresh Gourmet Cheese Crisps—use on salads instead of croutons
- [ ] Moon cheese
- [ ] Stur brand liquid water enhancer
- [ ] True Lemon and True Lime
- [ ] La Croix
- [ ] Zevia
- [ ] Field Day salsa
- [ ] Reduced Sugar ketchup
- [ ] No sugar added spaghetti sauce; we like Classico Riserva
- [ ] Old Fashioned oats
- [ ] Swerve and Pyure brand sweeteners
- [ ] Natural peanut butter
- [ ] Sprouts Splits pretzels
- [ ] Bolthouse yogurt-based dressing
- [ ] Josh Wine
- [ ]

Grocery List

- [ ]
- [ ]
- [ ]
- [ ]
- [ ]
- [ ]
- [ ]
- [ ]
- [ ]
- [ ]
- [ ]
- [ ]
- [ ]
- [ ]
- [ ]
- [ ]
- [ ]
- [ ]
- [ ]

- [ ]
- [ ]
- [ ]
- [ ]
- [ ]
- [ ]
- [ ]
- [ ]
- [ ]
- [ ]
- [ ]
- [ ]
- [ ]
- [ ]
- [ ]
- [ ]
- [ ]
- [ ]
- [ ]

Grocery List

Grocery List

The three possible plates for your meal

THE BLACK PLATE

Protein + Fat(s)

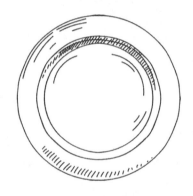

THE WHITE PLATE

Protein + Carbohydrates and starches

THE GRAY PLATE

Protein + Fat(s) + Carbohydrates/starches
(4-5 of these per week max)

FATS

Neutral Choices

UNLIMITED/EITHER PLATE

CARBS/STARCHES

FATS	UNLIMITED/EITHER PLATE	CARBS/STARCHES
nuts and nut butters	spices	sprouted breads
avocado	lemons & limes	sprouted cereal
butter	berries	blue corn chips
cheese	asparagus	old fashioned oats
cream	broccoli	apples
mayo	cabbage	apricots
oils	cauliflower	bananas
whole eggs	celery	grapes
full fat meats	cucumber	kiwi
chocolate	egg plant	melon
ice cream *	green beans	oranges/tangerines
nut flour	all greens	peaches
	mushrooms	nectarines
	onions	pears
	peppers	pineapple
	sprouts	plums
	squash	popcorn
	tomatoes (salsa)	quinoa
	zucchini	rice (brown, wild)
	Dreamfields pasta	beans
	Okios 000 yogurt	hummus
	Low carb/Whole wheat	lentils
	Mission wraps	carrots
		corn
		potatoes (sweet)
		WASA crackers (4)

*Bryers Carb Smart
and no sugar added coconut dream

Exercise Log Beginner

exercise	# of reps	total time	notes
jumping jacks			
pushups			
sit-ups			
1-minute plank			
30 sec side plank			
lunges			
squats			
straight leg lifts			
1-min wall sit			
high knees			
hip thrusts			
butterfly kicks			
mountain climbers			
jumping rope			

sprint distance: sprint time:

Workout Log

Mon___ Tue ___ Wed ___ Thu ___ Fri ___ Sat ___ Sun ___

Exercises	Sets	Reps	Wt	Sets	Reps	Wt	Sets	Reps	Wt	Sets	Reps	Wt	Sets	Reps	Wt

Jasinda's Reset:

FOR THOSE TIMES WHEN YOU JUST NEED A KICK-START.

IF YOU FEEL AS IF YOU JUST CAN'T GET THE HANG OF WHICH ORDER TO DO YOUR PLATES IN, BELOW IS A version I think works well for the long term. If you're struggling with not getting your metabolism moving as fast as you would like, or if you just aren't feeling so great, this combination might be helpful to you.

I like to do this combination with as little dairy on my black plates as possible—think a sprinkle of cheese instead of a full cup. You can still have it, just cut back on your cheese, cream, and any other dairy for one week and see how you feel. I also try to limit myself to just one snack a day when I'm doing this little reset. If I get the munchies, I'll snack on some non-starchy veggies or berries. Keep your movement normal and don't forget to drink lots of water; I like to infuse mine with some lemon and lime.

- Day 1: B-B-B
- Day 2: B-W-B
- Day 3: B-W-B
- Day 4: W-B-B
- Day 5: B-W-B
- Day 6: W-B-B
- Day 7: B-B-W

You can come back to this whenever you need a week of reset. Sometimes we can get too much dairy, which can block us up or slow us down, and I think this is a nice little break for our body. I know mine really likes it.

BE PROUD!

Made in the USA
Monee, IL
30 September 2020

43562307R00090